OTHER POGO BOOKS

POGO'S SUNDAY PUNCH

THE POGO PARTY

THE POGO SUNDAY BOOK

POTLUCK POGO

POGO PEEK-A-BOOK

THE INCOMPLEAT POGO

THE POGO STEPMOTHER GOOSE

THE POGO PAPERS

UNCLE POGO SO-SO STORIES

I GO POGO

POGO

WALT KELLY

POSITIVELY POGO

SIMON AND SCHUSTER • NEW YORK

A WORD TO THE FORE

The antics which have been drawn together in this book are huddled here for mutual protection like sheep. If they had half a wit apiece each would bound off in many directions to unsimplify the target.

These continue to be wondrous times when every man tries to find a formula for keeping the stranger's fingers from his throat. The simple expedient of holding hands will someday occur to a couple of people who will forever after be forgotten. We need to read and to think and to study the faces of our friends . . . a peaceful pursuit. But, in the light of our trial bombs bursting in air and the flash of the practice red rockets' glittering glare, the study of peace is a blinky business. This collection of strips reflects the skulking state of mind of one startled student.

W. K.

Here is a clutch of Odds and Ends,
Of Staggers, Leaps and Bobs and Bends,
Foolish, fretful, feeble, fancy,
For a Kelly, name of Nancy.

CONTENTS

Preface   11

Chapters

1 Merrily, Merrily,   13
2 O'er the Lea,   16
3 Verily, Verily,   21
4 Blue.   28

5 Raggedly, Baggedly,   33
6 Through the True,   36
7 Haggardly, Haggardly,   43
8 Flee.   47

9 Quickedly, Wickedly,   53
10 Shy and Low,   62
11 Higglety, Pigglety,   66
12 Play.   71

13	Happily, Flappily,	78
14	Mock the May,	83
15	Rapidly, Vapidly,	91
16	Blow.	100
17	Gimpily, Simpily,	101
18	Crow the Cry,	108
19	Dimpily, Limpily,	111
20	Do.	117
21	Hoppingly, Stoppingly,	123
22	Stow the Stew,	130
23	Moppily, Sloppily,	138
24	Fry.	147
25	Startedly, Heartedly,	152
26	See the Sea,	156
27	Markedly, Starkedly,	163
28	Bray.	168
29	Knitfully, Knackfully,	173
30	Know the Nay,	179
31	Pitifully, Witifully,	184
32	Plea.	189

Preface

YEP- P.T. AN' TAMANANNY IS GOIN' OUT OF SHOW BUSINESS INTO TEEVY.

THAT REMIND ME OF A OL' STORY- A FELLA SAY "IS A CARTOONIST A NEWS PAPER MAN?"

AN' HIS BOSS ANSWER... "IS A BARNACLE A SHIP?" HAW HAW HAW! OL' HARRY HERSHFIELD TOLE ME THAT'N HOO BOY!

A ROUSER! EVIDENTLY.

WOW!

FELLA SAYS "DOES A CARTOONIST WORK FOR A NEWSPAPER?" AND HIS BOSS SAYS "BARNACLES"-UH-MM-"BARNACLES" UH UM-WELL, HE TOLE HIM "BARNACLES TO YOU, JACK·····BARNACLES!"

SERVED HIM RIGHT, TOO.

BOY OH BOY OH BOY OH BOY OH BOY!

HA! YOU DOG! HOLD ON THERE, VARLET, ERE I CARVE YOU STEM TO STERN.

OH, PLEASE SIR, SPARE ME, FOR I AM BUT A SIMPLE MAIDEN!

NAY··· YOU ARE A SPY!

15

18

19

CHAPTER

3

Verily, Verily,

DO YOU *GOTTA* LOOK LIKE *THAT*?

A MAN CAN'T HELP HIS *OWN* NATURAL BEAUTY, SON.

PERSON'LY I IS *QUIETLY* PROUD...

QUIETLY?

THAT *BATHIN'* SUIT IS SO LOUD IT SKEERS THE *FISHES*.

IT WAS LEFT ME BY MY PA-- A MAN OF *EX*-QUIZZLE TASTE.

GLAD TO HEAR IT--I WAS THINKIN' IT LOOK LIKE THE TOP HALF OF YOU *EX*-CAPED FROM THE *STATE BASTILLE*.

COME TO THINK OF IT, PA *DID* SAY A *GUMMINT BLOODHOUND* WAS IN POSSESSION OF THE *DRAWERS*.

I JES' HAD A *SHOCK*!

SO IS I.

THAT SO? SAME ONE AS ME? IS YOU HEARD THAT *NO DOGS* IS ALLOWED TO PLAY THE PART OF A *DOG* ON THE *TEEVY*?

NO, BUT I CAUGHT A GLIMPSE OF YO' *PANTS*.

OH, **THEM**--? THEY'S MY DADDY'S **BATHIN' DRAWERS**-- HE WHUPPED 'EM OFFA A EX-CAPIN' OCCUPANT OF THE **CALABAZOO** WHEN HE WAS IN GUMMINT WORK.

A OUTLAW LIKE THAT OUGHT TO BE **PURSOOT** AN' **CAUGHT** JUST TO MAKE HIM **TAKE** BACK THEM **BATHIN' TROUSERS.**

BUT HOW COULD HE BE FOUND **NOW**?

FUNNY THING HOW I COME INTO THESE **BATHIN' DRAWERS**-- PA PULLED 'EM OFF A EX-CAPIN' CONVICK --AN'--

HEIGHDY

HEIGHDY

TOODLE OO.

FUNNY THING HOW I COME INTO THIS **BATHIN' SUIT** --- PA LEFT IT TO ME CLAIMIN' IT WAS PART OF A SET AN'--

WHAT ?!

WAIT! YOU NEEDS **ARTIOFFICIAL---**

I DON'T WANT NOTHIN' **ARTIFICIAL**...I WANTS THE REAL THING OR **NOTHIN'!**

JUMP IN AN' RESCUE **HIM** NOW---- **TURN AN' TURN ABOUT**---YOU TWO KIN MAKE THIS **LIFE GUARDIN' JOB** LAST **ALL** SUMMER, IF YOU PLAYS YO' CARDS RIGHT.

HOW'LL I HOLD UP MY BATHIN' DRAWERS?

THEY IS BEEN TIMES WHEN I IS BEEN **SORRY** I WAS A ALLIGATOR BUT, **BY JING**, I NEVER BEEN AS **SORRY** AS **YOU** SHOULD BE SORRY----

I'M NOT SORRY I'M A ALLIGATOR 'CAUSE I **AIN'T! I'M A DOG.**

ALL THE MORE REASON---**YOU OUGHT** TO BE **SORRY** YOU **AIN'T** SORRY TO BE SORRY YOU AIN'T A **ALLIGATOR** STEAD OF A **SORRY DOG.**

I'M **SORRY 'BOUT NOTHIN'!**

THAT'S JES' IT--- YOU IS SORRY 'BOUT BEIN' **NOTHIN'**--I'M SORRY YOU IS SORRY BUT SORRIER THAT YOU AIN'T SORRY 'BOUT BEIN' SORRY TO BE SORRY 'BOUT THE OTHER SORRY THING YOU OUGHT TO BE SORRY OF ---

DEEP DOWN, I **IS** SORRY..

'BOUT WHAT?

THAT'S WHAT I **IS** SORRY 'BOUT-- ---I **DUNNO.**

26

CHAPTER

4

Blue.

YOU CAN TEACH ME TO BE A *RED WHITE AN' BLUE BLOODED DOG* OR NOTHIN'!!

FAW.

VERY WELL FOR *YOU* TO SAY "FAW"--BUT *WHAT AM I* GONE SAY WHEN I GOTTA *BARK* IN A *FOREIGN LANGUAGE?* YOU WANTS ME TO BE A *KOMONDOR* AND I DON'T KNOW A WORD OF *FRENCH*.

YOU WOON'T NEED IT.

WELL-- IN *THAT* CASE--IF I COULD BARK IN AMERICAN I *MIGHT* CONSIDER TRYIN' OUT--

THE *KOMONDOROK* (WHICH IS THE PLURAL OF YOU) IS DESCENT FROM THE *AFTSCHARKA*-- YOU'D HAFTA BARK IN *MAGYAR*.

MAGYAR? WHERE WAS *THIS* DOG FOUND?

ON THE *STEPPES*.

OF *WHOSE* STOOP?

THIS BOOK ON "*TRAINING THE NOBLE DOG*" GOT A LOT IN IT ABOUT THE *KOMONDOROK*.

ATBLER

SEEM LIKE BEIN'*THIS* DOG IS JUST CUT OUT FOR YOU -- IT SAY HE GOT A *FIERCE BUILD* ON HIM --*SQUARE SHOULDERS* AN' A *HANDSOME HEAD*--

29

30

MY *word*, BUT YOU ARE A *DEAD RINGER for my OLD* GEOMETRY TEACHER!

AN' *YOU* IS A DEAD RINGER FOR A **BONE HEAD.**

GENTLEMEN, GENTLEMEN—**PLEASE!** *ALBERT,* HERE, IS LEARNING TO PLAY THE PART OF A **DOG** ... A **FOREIGN** *TEEVY* STAR.

MM— LET US HEAR A FOREIGN *BARK,* SIR.

CINCHONA! CINCHONA! CINCHONA! CINCHONA!

GREAT!! GREAT!! *CARRY ON!* IT'S A *REAL* AU NATUREL

CINCHONA IS A *FOREIGN BARK?*

CERT'LY ... THEY MAKES QUININE OUTEN IT -- *ANY* SWAMP CRITTUR KNOW *THAT!*

MEBBE MIZ MA'M'SELLE HEPZIBAH KNOWS HOW TO BARK IN *MAGYAR* -- HOW'S THE **KOMONDOROK** GO, MIZ MA'M'SELLE?

THESE SONG I DO NOT KNOW -- BUT THERE ARE A SWEET **SMALL SONG** ALL 'BOUT GIRL WHAT IS LOSE HER **LIVER** ON BANKS OF SEINE.

DON'T YOU MEAN HER LOVER !?

NON! SHE IS CAT FANCIER AN' TRAP CAT WITH LIVER -- POOF. ONE DAY SHE LOSE TWO POUNDS AN' HALF AN' SO SHE SING SAD SONG 'BOUT HIM *LA LA LA LA LA LA* ♫♫ LIKE SO...

THE **KOMONDOROK** AIN'T A **SONG** - IT'S A BREED OF DOG - FROM **HUNGARY**.

I'M GONE **BE ONE**.

DOES THE GOVERMENS AT BUDAPEST KNOW THESE NEWS?

'COURSE I WOONENT HAFTA BE **ANY** PARTICKLER FOREIGN DOG...JES' SO'S I IS GLAMMERD UP SOME.

HOW WOULD A **FRENCH** DOG BARK, MA'M'SELLE?

I KNOW NICE DOG WHO IS CALL **PAPILLONS**.

AN' HE GO:

TUT TUT TUT TUT TUT TUT

HE PRONOUNCE THESE IN **FRANCAIS**, NATUREL, AN' HE ARE SMALL, **TINY, LITTLE** ANIMAL DOG USE FOR COTCH THE **BOOSTERFLIES**...

MAN! I'M GLAD SHE DIN'T IMITATE A **BIG DOG!**

SHE SURE GIVE **ME** A TURN, FRIEND...

MENS! FOOF!

CHAPTER

5

Raggedly, Baggedly,

WHAT *ELEGANCE!* SUCH SYMBOLIC AN' SYMPATHETIC SYMMETRY OF LINE-- *A JOY* TO *EYE* AND *EAR.*

HMM-- YOU RUN ACROSS ONE OF *SHAKSPERE'S LOST FOLIOS?*

NO-- IT'S MY NEXT *SINGIN' COMMERCIAL!* OH, I LOVE IT--- JES' LOVE LOVE LOVE *LOVE* IT!

♪♫ MORE PRECIOUS THAN GOLD BUT LESS THAN A DOLLAR-- MOST FRESHEST AN' COLD IS *KOKOMO KOLA.*" ♫

YOU'LL GOTTA *CHANGE* THE SONG-- KOLA AN' DOLLAR DON'T RHYME.

CHANGE THE SONG, *MY EYE!* *I'LL* CHANGE THE *PRODUCT-- -COLLAR* AN' DOLLAR RHYMES, DON'T IT?

A *COLD KOKOMO KOLLAR?*

I DON'T LIKE TO BE A *WET BLANKET* BUT YO' SINGIN' COMMERCIALS IS ON A *REEF.*

IF YOU DON'T LIKE BEIN' LIKE YOU SAY WHY IS YOU *ALWAYS* WHAT YOU *SAID?*

BUT FRIEND OF MY YOUTH, COMPANION OF MY CRADLE, YO' COMMERCIALS DON'T MAKE *SENSE!*

THAT IS A REE-QUIREMENT NOT HITHERTO ENFORCED ON LAND, AT SEA OR ON THE *AIR!*

BALDERDASH.!--LISTEN TO THIS *FAMOUS SINGIN' COMMERCIAL--* "COME, ALL YOU YOUNG SPORTS COME EAT UP YOUR **WARTS** FOR THAT IS THE WAY TO GROW!"

ACK! WARTS?

NOT **REAL WARTS,** STUPID-- WARTS SPELLED *BACKWARDS* IS "*STRAW*", THAT BONE BUILDING BELOVED CEREAL FAVORED BY YOUNG AND OLD--*ANYBODY* KNOWS THAT--'CAUSE IT MAKES **SENSE!**

WHAT'S "UGH" SPELT BACKWARDS?

I S'POSE YOU IS HEERD THE **BIG NEWS?** CHURCHY AN' ME IS GONNA MAKE A **FORTUNE--** WE'LL SELL HIS SINGIN' COMMERCIALS TO THE **TEEVY PEOPLE..**

OH, I **KNOW,** HEH HEH--*YOU'RE* GONNA SAY IF HE COUNTERBUTES THE **SONGS--***WHAT'S I COUNTERBUTE?* MY **BRAINS,** FRIENDS-- IT TAKES A HEAD TO GET AHEAD, HEH HEH?

GONNA USE *YOUR* HEAD, HUH?

WULL----*MEBBE* YOU GOT A **POINT** THERE, OWL--

AN' IF YOU COMBS YO' **HAIR** JES' RIGHT *NOBODY* 'LL NOTICE.

Through the True,

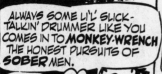

ALWAYS SOME LI'L SLICK-TALKIN' DRUMMER LIKE YOU COMES IN TO **MONKEY-WRENCH** THE HONEST PURSUITS OF **SOBER** MEN.

YEAH!

WHY, OH, **WHY** DO THOSE OF US WHO EARNESTLY BEND OUR **FRAIL** BUT **COURAGEOUS** EFFORTS TO BENEFIT EVERYONE IN EVERY WALK OF LIFE **CARING NOT** FOR OUR SELFS **ALONE** BUT **INWARDLY BLEEDING** ....

AND SUFFERING IN AN **UNSTINTING** AND **SELF EFFACING** NOBILITY OF GENEROSITY SET WITH THE **DIAMONDS** AND **PEARLS** OF **LOVE**, LOVE FOR OUR FELLOWS AND KNOWLEDGE OF OUR OWN UNBECOMING ....

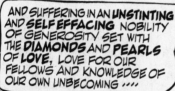

UM· UH·· **WHERE WAS I?**

WHERE WAS YOU **WHEN?**

YOU TAXIED DOWN THE **RUNWAY** AND DUMPED YOUR **GAS** SO'S YOU COULD **TAKE OFF!**

WE WAS SEARCHIN' FOR **"BOW-WOW"** IN GERMAN WHEN YOU COME IN **BE-LITTLIN'** OUR SCHOLARLY QUEST.

WAU WAU

WHY DO YOU SAY **"VOW VOW,"** FRIEND?

'CAUSE THAT'S THE WAY YOU BARKS IN **GERMAN.**

VOW-VOW? DOGS PRONOUNCE THEIR "V'S" IN GERMAN?

YEP.. I ONCE HAD A JOB AS A DOG IN A SMALL GERMAN BUTCHER SHOP.

WHAT? YOU WAS A DOG..? WHAT'D YOU CHASE, WEEVILS?

NOPE.. THIS WAS SUCH A SMALL SHOP IN GERMAN EAST AFRICA...NO ROOM FOR A DOG....SO, TO KEEP THE ELEPHANTS AWAY FROM THE COLD-CUTS I OFFERED MY SERVICES AND....

THIS PLACE WHERE I HAD THE JOB BEIN' THE DOG OF IN AFRICA TO KEEP THE ELEPHANTS OUTEN THE ICE-BOX WAS A HANGOUT FOR ALL KINDS WEIRD AN' EXOTIC TROPICAL CREATURES.

WHAT WITH THE BOER WAR BEIN' OVER WHICH I WON ON A SECRET MISSION EVERY BODY HAD NOTHIN' TO DO BUT HUNG AROUND THE STORE ALL DAY EATIN' CHEESE AN' PICKLES.

WHEN MEIN STADTHOLDER WHO WAS BOSS-MAN COMPLAINED ABOUT THE SALAMI BEIN' A TARGET TOO OFTEN, THESE HANGERS-ON WOULD BITE MR. STADTHOLDER UNTIL HE LOOKED LIKE A SWISS CHEESE HISSELF WHICH HE COULDN'T OF BEEN BECAUSE OF BEIN' GERMAN.

SO, FROM LIVERWURST AN' INK I CONCOCTED A SNAKE BITE CURE KNOWED AS RAWSON'S-OWN WHICH WAS POPULAR WITH ALL THE SNAKES AN'· WHAT?

I SAID WE'D LIKE SOME TALKIN' ROOM.

40

I'LL JUST SHOW ONE OF THESE **APPRENTICE COBRAS** OF YOURS THE FAMOUS JUDO HOLD WHICH I LEARNT YOU -- **FIRST THING** IS THEY ALWAYS GOTTA FIND OUT IS THEY ALWAYS GOTTA BE **ALERT**--

IF THEY KIN JUST KEEP IN MIND NEVER TO BE **TOOK BY SURPRISE**-- THEY GOTTA LEARN THE WORLD IS FULL OF SNEAKY TYPES ALWAYS READY TO BE --

-- UNFAIR!

SEE! NOW LET THAT BE A LESSON TO YOU.

THIS WORM CHILE IS **SHARP** BUT WATCH HOW I TEACH HIM THE FLASHY HOLD I LEARNT TO YOU--

WAIT A MINUTE.

DON'T WORRY, HE WON'T SNEAK UP **MY** REAR AGAIN -- AND UH-- **WOOP!**

LIKE I SAY.. WAIT, WAIT!

41

NO FAIR! NO FAIR! I WAS ATTACKED BY **TWO** OF 'EM.

YOU WAS NOT--THE ONE WHAT **THROWS** YOU IS THE **SAME ONE** YOU'RE S'POSED TO BE TEACHIN'.

PHOO! WHAT'S THE **DIFFERENCE** BETWEEN 'EM? **I** CAN'T TELL 'EM APART.

NOTHIN' TO IT.. --THESE OTHER TWO IS GIRLS.

HOWDY, GENTS! WE'S GONE HAVE A FRY AN' I'M LOOKIN' FOR **VOLUNTEERS** TO DIG A **LITTLE BAIT.**

MM -- WELL, WELL - YES INDEED - MM HM

I'D BE **GLAD** TO HELP BUT I HURT MY **ARM** SHOWIN' THE **APPRENTICE COBRAS** HOW TO **DEE**-FEND THEIRSELFS AGAINST SNEAKS, CUT PURSES AN' OTHER RIP JACKS.

ME TOO.

YOU HURT **YOUR** ARM, SNAVELY?

NO ---BUT WATCHIN' MOUSE HERE WAS A **TRAUMATIC EXPERIENCE** OF SUCH **BOISTEROUS** PROPORTIONS THAT I-- - **UH**- THE **CHILDREN** HERE MIGHT LIKE TO DIG A --

THEY'S **RUN OFF!** WHAT **SOME** PEOPLE WON'T **DO** TO **AVOID WORK!**

THEM WORMS KNOWS THE ANGLES.

CHAPTER

7

Haggardly, Haggardly,

NOW IN *THIS* SPOT, YOU, *FLOSSIE THE NOBLE DOG*, BURST INTO **POLICE HQ** WITH THE **GENTLE JASMINIA** IN YOUR MOUTH ···· THE CAPTAIN SAYS ···

"*THIS* GIRL HAS BEEN **DRUGGED!**" AND *YOU* SAY "I KNOW··

I DONE DRUG HER ALL THE WAY FROM PEACH TREE STREET!

OH THIS STUFF IS TOO RICH ···· TOO *RICH*·· *TOO GOOD FOR TEEVY* ···· IT DESERVES A *BETTER FATE!*

TURN IT OVER TO **FORT KNOX** AND LET 'EM BURY IT FOR YOU.

WELL, *THAT* PROVES IT ···· *OUR* HUMOR AIN'T APPRECIATED AROUND *HERE*·· THE WAY THEY RUNS *THIS* STRIP NOBODY LAUGHS AT NOTHIN' *REAL FUNNY* ···· JUST AT **CUTE** STUFF.

PORKY DIN'T EVEN SMILE WHEN ME, **FLOSSIE THE DOG**, BRINGS THE GIRL INTO H.Q. AN' THE CAP'N SAYS "*SHE BEEN DRUGGED!*"·· AN' I SAYS "I KNOW·· I **DRUG** HER ALL THE WAY FROM **CANAL STREET!**"

URF! URF! URF!

YOU'S *LAUGHIN'* PORKY··· YOU **GITS** THAT JOKE FROM YESTERDAY!

NO·· BUT THE WITTY STORY OF LAST WEEK, "*WHO WAS THE LADY EYE SORE WITH YOU LAST NIGHT?*" NOW STRIKES ME AS **EXTREMELY** DROLL···· ESPECIALLY IF THERE IS SOME SORT OF FUNNY REPLY.

THE KIND OF A DOG ALBERT OUGHT TO BE IS A *BOXER*.

I'M **SURE** HE'LL APPRECIATE THE SUGGESTION.

YOU SAY ALBERT OUGHT TO BE A *BOXER*? AN' BARK IN GUTTURAL REMARKS! *THAT REE-MIND ME OF SOMETHIN' WE GONE USE ON THE "FLOSSIE, THE NOBLE DOG" SHOW!*

MUMF!

FELLOW WINS TWO **ELEPHANTS** IN A RAFFLE AN' BRINGS 'EM HOME TELLIN' HIS WIFE THEY IS **DOGS**... "WHAT KIND DOGS IS **THESE**?" SHE ASKS... "**BOXERS**," HE SAY, "CAN'T YOU SEE THEIR **TRUNKS**?"

WOW

HOW ABOUT A LITTLE COURTEOUS "HA-HA"?

RIDICULOUS ON THE **FACE** OF IT... **WHO** WOULD RAFFLE OFF A PAIR OF **ELEPHANTS**?

WOW WOW

ONE MEBBE BUT **TWO**...?

SNAVELY AN' THE MOUSE TELLS ME YOU GOT A NEW JOKE 'BOUT **BOXERS**.

I COME OVER TO HEAR IT HOPIN' IT'S THE ONE ABOUT THE FELLOW SAYS HE'S A **BOXER**... ON ACCOUNT HE JES' GOT A JOB CRATIN' MUSHMELONS... **I ALLUS LAUGHS AT THAT'N SO SHOOT!**

NO... **THIS'N** IS 'BOUT A FELLOW BRINGS HOME TWO **ELEPHANTS** AN' TELLS HIS WIFE THEY IS **DOGS**... **BOXERS**, HE SAY... ON ACCOUNT OF LOOK AT THEIR TRUNKS...

NOPE... I DUNNO **THAT'N**... BUT THAT OTHER'S A **FAVORITE OF MINE**... I LAUGHS TWO OR THREE GOOD HEARTY LICKS AT IT IF'N I HEAR IT...

46

CHAPTER

8

Flee.

I JUST HAD A **GREAT IDEA!** *PROBLY* THE FINEST TYPE IDEA OF THE **LOCAL SEASON**

GO EASY. GO EASY.

WHY GO EASY? I GOT A **GREAT** IDEA FOR THE KIND OF **DOG** **ALBERT** OUGHT TO BE .. A IDEA WHAT SHOULD BE SHARED WITH THE **NATION** .. A IDEA TO BE GIVE OUT TO MEBBE A HUNNERD AND SIXTY MILLION SOULS AN' ....

AN' MEBBE I'D MAKE A FEW **MILLION PESOS** OR POSSIBLY WIN A SPOT ON SOME **GUMMINT BODY** ....

REMEMBER THE **LAST TIME** YOU TRIED THIS THE **BLUE COATS** TRIED TO PUT YOU IN THE **DEEP FREEZE** FOR SIX MOONS.

PHOOF .. I **STILL** SEE NOTHING WRONG WITH PRINTING *EDIBLE* MONEY.

BUT NOT ON THIN SLICES OF **CHEESE** .. ESPECIALLY WITH **HOLES** IN IT ..

WHAT IS THIS **FOURTEEN KARAT STERLING** IDEA 'BOUT WHAT KIND OF A **DOG** ALBERT OUGHT TO BE?

NO - NO. YOU BELITTLED **MY** MONEY PLAN! CLAIMED BILLS PRINTED ON ANYTHING BUT PAPER WAS *DE RIGUEUR MORTIS* FOR WHOMSOEVER WAS CAUGHT.

BUT, DEAR BOY, THE **MONEY CONCESSION** IN THE GUMMINT IS GUARDED **VERY JEALOUSLY.**

WHO ELSE EVER OFFERED TO PRINT IT ON **CHEESE?** **NOBODY!** NOT EVEN HOLLAND!

CHAPTER

9

Quickedly, Wickedly,

JUST **THINK!** IF WE MADE **MONEY** OUT OF **FOOD** PEOPLE WOULD USE MORE OF IT~~**BUSINESS** WOULD **BOOM!**

PENSACOLA · IT'S THE SPA

YOU FIGGER TO MAKE MONEY A **HOUSEHOLD** WORD?

PENSACOLA IT'S THE SPA

WULL ··

WHAT HOUSEHOLD WORD WOULD YOU **MAKE** IT? *SPIGOT, CELLAR, FRYIN'PAN~~CUPBOARD~~ JELLY JAR~~DOG COLLAR*? ALL **THEM** IS USED ··· WHAT ELSE **IS** THERE?

BLUB

AIN'T YOU WORKIN' ON **TEEVY** COMMERCIALS?

NOPE·· I'SE GONE OUTTA *THAT* LINE·· POGO'S IN CONFINEMENT· WE DIRTIED HIS LAST SHIRT.

HE'S YOUR NEW PARTNER?

NOT **EGG**- ZACKLY HE MORE OF A CON- SULTAN.

HOW 'BOUT *THIS'N* FOR OUR SHOW····? A MAN STRIPS THE BARK OFF'N *THREE BIRCH TREES* TO MAKE A CANOE-···OTHER FELLOW SAYS "*THEM'S MINE! YOU* IS BARKED UP THE WRONG *THREE!*"

GET IT?

I IS LEAVIN'···· GONE JOIN P.T. AN' TAMMANANNY.

THAT LAST ONE WAS THE CAMEL WHAT BROKE MY BACK.

WAIT FOR ME! I 'GREES WITH YOU! DON'T LEAVE ME ALONE WITH THEM JOKES!

TAMANANNY AN' P.T. WILL BE *OVER*-JOYED TO SEE US ····INASMUCH AS THEY IS GOIN' INTO *TEEVY* THEY'LL NEED *OUR* HELP···AN' THEY *LOVES* US, SO.

MAYBE THEY'LL SAY THEY IS ALL *FULL UP* ···OR WE AIN'T GOT *NO* EXPERIENCE····

BUT THEY AN' WE IS OLD FRIENDS! WOULD THEY ACT LIKE *THAT?*

WE BEEN DESERTED.... *LEFT* IN THE LURCH.

AND *RIGHT* AT THE CHURCH.

WOE IS *US*, FRIEND.... W-H-O-WOE.

WE WAS PERTY *WOED-UP* WHEN US GOT THE *BAD* NEWS.

NOBODY PAYS US NO MIND.... P.T. AND *TAMANANNY* IS RUN OFF AN' THE OTHERS JES' *SCORN* US.... I TELL YOU, ALBERT, I'M GLAD I GOT *ONE TRUE* AN' *NOBLE FRIEND.*

AN'.... *TEE-HEE!* TOO-HOO! *WHO* WOULD *THAT BE,* PRAY TELL?

ME

DOES YOU *IM*-PLY THAT ONLY *YOU* IS FIT TO BE A FRIEND OF YOURN?

ALBERT, YOU GOTTA REMEMBER *WHO* IS MAN'S *BEST FRIEND*--THE NOBLE *DOG* IS, NATURAL, AN' *WHO* IS THE NOBLE DOG EVEN A FRIEND OF BETTER'N ANYBODY OF? *THE NOBLE DOG,* BUT OF COURSE--

CHAPTER

10

Shy and Low,

CHAPTER

11

Higglety, Pigglety,

THAT'S NICE.

WELL! THAT'S EE-NUFF FOR ME!

NOBODY LAUGHS AT OUR JOKES.

THAT PROVES YOU HATES US ···· YOU LAUGHS AT EVERYBODY ELSE'S JOKES···· EVEN ONES IN OTHER COMICAL STRIPS.

BUT I DIN'T KNOW WHAT YOU TOLE WAS A JOKE···· YOU NEVER TELLS ME THAT PART.

IT IS TRUE THAT HE SAID IT WAS NICE.

THAT'S ANOTHER INSULT···· POGO TAKE SO MUCH STING OFF'N EVER'THING HE SAY THAT A SIMPLE GOODNIGHT FROM HIM COULD BE ANOTHER MAN'S: DROP DEAD!

SO, BY "NICE," HE MEANS····?

THE SHAMEFUL WAY WE BEEN TREATED IS SO *SHAMEFUL* IT'S ENOUGH TO MAKE A *MAN COMMIT SUICIDE.*

RIGHT! BUT WHICH MAN?

HON. MIKE LAPINE

IN FACT, FRIEND, IT'D SERVE THESE *NUMP-HODS* AROUND HERE RIGHT IF *ONE OF US DID* COMMIT SUICIDE! THEN THEY'D CHANGE THEIR TUNE.

TO WHAT?

TO A *FUNERAL MARCH,* I GUESS-- ONLY THING IS I'D MISS YOU *SO* WHEN I DOES IT.

I'LL MISS *YOU,* TOO-- JES' MAKE SURE YOU WRITES FROM WHERE-*SO*-EVER YOU GOES "PERVIDIN" IT'S *COOL ENOUGH.*

I AIN'T GOIN' *ANYWHERES!* YOU DIN'T THINK I WAS GONE *START RIGHT OUT* COMMITTIN' SUICIDE ON *MY OWN LOVIN' SELF?*

WELL, YOU AIN'T GONE *WARM UP* ON *ME,* SON.

WHY DOES *WE* ALLUS GIT ALL THE *BUM* BREAKS?

WELL, WE CAN'T HAVE *EVER THING,* GOOD LOOKS, CHARM, BRAINS AN' PERFECT PITCH---

RIGHT.

MISS MARIANNA

THE *BEST BREAK* ANYBODY EVER GETS IS IN BEIN' *ALIVE* IN THE FIRST PLACE.

AN' YOU DON'T UNNERSTAN' WHAT A **PERFECT DEAL** IT IS UNTIL YOU REALIZES THAT YOU AIN'T GONE BE **STUCK** WITH IT FOREVER, EITHER.

IT'S PERFECKLY ALL RIGHT FOR **PORKYPINE** TO SAY THE BEST **BREAK** YOU GITS IS **FIRST** BEIN' **ALIVE** AN' THEN IN NOT BEIN' **STUCK** WITH IT **BUT--**

HOLE THIS A MINUTE?

--HE **FERGITS** THAT WHEN A MAN GITS HANDED A **LONG** LIFE HE STANDS A GOOD CHANCE OF **STARVIN'** TO DEATH A-FORE IT'S OVER.

IT'S A **FRIGHTENIN'** THOUGHT.

HEY! DOES YOU TWO WANNA GIT THE **RAW FISH COBBLES?** THEM BRIM FISHES AIN'T MORE'N WARMED UP.

CHAPTER

12

Play.

MEBBE YOU KNOWS THAT FUNNY STORY 'BOUT THE FELLA WHAT WAS A **BOXER** 'CAUSE HE HAD A JOB **BOXIN' MUSHMELONS.**

UM

I CERT'LY WOULD **AD-MIRE** TO HEAR IT 'CAUSE IT **ALLUS** CHEERS ME UP ··· IT'S MY **FAVORITE JOKE** ··· GO AHEAD AN' TELL IT IF YOU KNOWS IT.

WELL

I KNOWS THE STORY 'BOUT THE FELLA WHAT TOLE EVERY-BODY HE WAS A **BOXER** 'CAUSE HE HAD A JOB **BOXIN' BLUEBERRIES** ··· CARE TO HEAR **THAT** ONE?

··OH·· MMM·· NO

IT WOULDN'T BE THE **SAME.** I ONLY ENJOYS THE OTHER ONE··· IT **ALLUS** GIVE ME WHAT IS CALLED A **BOFF.**

TOO BAD·· YOU ALLUS LAUGH IN THE KEY OF **F SHARP** AN' I WANTED TO **TUNE** THIS THING.

HERE'S WHERE THEY TOLE ME **OL' MOUSE** LIVES AN' SURE 'NOUGH THERE'S HIS **MAIL BOX.**

MOUSE

MAILBOX, BUT NO **HOUSE** ···MEBBE HE JES' STOP BY FOR HIS MAIL.

MOUSE

73

I IS *THRU WITH YOU*...I IS SOCIALLY OSTRICH-SIZIN' YOU FROM MY LIST.

GO AHEAD! WE BEEN *DID* TO LIKE WHAT YOU SAY BY MORE FANCY PEOPLE THAN *YOU IS!*

PERSON'LY I COMED OVER TO FIND OUT WHAT *SURE-FIRE* PLAN IT WAS YOU GIVE *CHURCHY* FOR MAKIN' MONEY.

UM

LET'S SEE..COULD IT OF BEEN FOR TRADIN' DOUGHNUT HOLES TO THE BUTTON HOLE PEOPLE? ..OR..UM..SAY, I HAD A *DANDY* FOR THIS *MOTORIZED AGE*...

DON'T GIVE THIS AWAY, PAL.. BUT *DRIVE-IN FUNERAL PARLORS* COULD BECOME A *LIVIN' RAGE*...QUICK, EASY CURB SERVICE AN'...

LOOK ME IN THE EYE AN' TELL ME *AGAIN* YOU THINKS *DRIVE-IN* FUNERAL PARLORS WOULD BE A GOOD IDEA.

WHY *SHOULD* I ? IF YOU DON'T KNOW A *GOOD BUSINESS* WHEN YOU HEARS IT ?

NEXT YOU'LL BE TELLIN' ME THEY COULD BE *SELF-SERVICE* OPERATIONS.

WHY NOT ?

74

FRIEND, YOU GOT VISION" TAKE MY PLAN FOR SICK SERVICES INCORPORATED. S'POSE YOU'RE SICK... YOU DON'T WANNA GO TO A DOC—

THAT'S WHERE I COME IN... I GO FOR YOU" I TELL HIM WHAT YOU FEEL LIKE -- HE EXAMINES ME.. GIVES ME THE MEDICINE -- NO HORRID AFTER TASTE FOR YOU ... QUICK, CONVENIENT --- NOTHING FOR YOU TO DO, SIR.

EXCEPT JUMP IN THE CAR AND LOOK FOR THAT DRIVE-IN FUNERAL PARLOR.

YOU SURE YOU CAN'T REMEMBER NO OTHER SCHEME 'CEPT THE DRIVE-IN FUNERAL PARLOR AN' SUBSTITUTE SICKNESS?

MOUSE

WHAT'S THE MATTER WITH DRIVE-IN FUNERAL PARLORS WITH SELF-SERVICE?

HOW CAN YOU EMBALM YOUR OWN SELF IF YOU'RE DEAD?

MMM. YES... THAT WOULD TAKE A LI'L' DOIN'...WELL, THAT RULES OUTEMBALMIN'. HOW ABOUT CRE-MATIN'?

ANY FOOL KNOWS YOU GOTTA BE ALIVE TO CREMATE YOUR SELF.

ANOTHER THING... WOULD ANYBODY DEAD PAY HIS BILL? WOULDN'T HE JES' LEAVE?

THE POINT IS.. WOULD YOU WANT HIM TO COME BACK WITH THE CASH?

"LONG AS A *DRIVE-IN FUNERAL PARLOR* IS OUT OF THE QUESTION, HOW ABOUT THAT *SICK-SERVICE* I DREAMED UP?"

HOW'D IT GO?

LIKE THIS *--LIE DOWN--* NOW I GOTTA PLAY *TWO PARTS--* FIRST I IS *SICK--* BUT YO' JOB IS TO TAKE MY PLACE-- TO SAVE *ME* THE TROUBLE OF HAVIN' A DOCTOR EXAMINE *ME* --- OKAY, NOW I IS THE DOCTOR--

WELL YOUNG MAN STICK OUT YO' TONGUE OOG IT LOOK LIKE LAS' WEEK'S FLYPAPER WELL HA HA NO USE GIVIN' UP HOPE IS THEY ANY *UNSANITY* IN YO' FAMBLY EITHER YOU AIN'T GOT NO PULSE OR MY WATCH IS STOPPED HO HO.

YOU AIN'T *GOT* NO WATCH! AN' ANYTHING I *HATES* IS A *HA-HA* TYPE OF MEDICAL MAN--*YOU* IS CHEERFUL ENOUGH TO BE A *UNDERTAKER--*

WHO'S SICK? *ME!* THAT'S WHO. I GITS ANY KIND DOCTOR I *WANTS* AN' BESIDES *YOU* GIVE ME *FOUR DOLLARS* FOR A HOME CALL!

ALL RIGHT, NOW WE REVERSE THE ROLES--*YOU TAKE MY* PLACE AS *PATIENT* AND *I'LL* BE THE *DOCTOR.*

I GUESS IT CAN'T BE HELPED THOUGH I FEEL SOUND AS A DOLLAR.

WHOOF! FIRST OF ALL TAKE YO' HAT OFF IN A SICKROOM--

SOME DOCTOR! YOU CRAWLS IN BED THE MINUTE YOU GITS HERE.

CHAPTER

13

Happily, Flappily,

IS THIS BOAT GOIN' UP TO **NEW YORK,** POGO....? COULD YOU ROW ME UP?

HECK, NO! THERE'S NOTHIN' UP THERE BUT PEOPLE--

AN' **BASEBALL**----THEY TELLS ME THE NEW BALL IS ACTUALLY A **JACK RABBIT**--- AN' I THUNK I'D GIT A JOB-

YOU COULDN'T GIT A JOB AS A **BASEBALL**-- THAT AIN'T WHAT THEY MEANS....*EVEN IF ANY-BODY COULD THROW YOU YOU'D NEVER LAST THRU BATTIN' PRACTICE.*

I GUESS YOU'RE RIGHT--COUSIN COTTONSIDES WENT UP ONE YEAR AN' HAD TO TAKE A JOB AS A **PIGEON** IN BRYANT PARK· WHAT A **COMEDOWN,** HIM A EXPERT ON RABBITTIN' AN' ALL.

THE CITY'S *FIERCE*

OL' JOHN DENSON

HERE COME OWL AN' MOUSE· PROB'LY JES' ACHIN' TO GIVE US A GAME OF BALL IN HONOR OF IT BEIN' **WORLD SERIES** TIME.

IT'S **WORLD SERIES TIME**·· US OUGHT TO BE GITTIN' INTO THE GAME.

GREAT.... I'LL PITCH.

YOU?

CERT'LY *ME!* DIN'T I USETA TRAVEL WITH THE OL' SAINT LOOEY BROWNS? (UNBEKNOWNST TO *THEM* OF COURSE)... BUT IF THEY'D OF PLAYED ME I'D OF STOLT EVERY BASE IN THE LEAGUE.

PHOO

IN MY *EXTREME YOUTH* I TRIED OUT WITH A FELLA NAMED McGRAW BUT HE CLAIMED MY KEY PLAY, STEALIN' FIRST BASE, WAS *ILLEGAL.*

SOME FOLKS JES' DON'T LIKE MICE, I GUESS.

MEBBE US *WILL* COME AN' PLAY IN THE WORLD SERIES...

SURE, DON'T BE MAD NO MORE... WE *NEEDS* YO' BAT.

GOT THE BAT RIGHT HERE WITH SOME *LOOSE JAM* AN' *BIRDS EGGS* I BEEN SAVIN'.

DID YOU HEAR OUR *UMPIRE* STORY, POGO?

NOPE

ALBERT

SEEMS THIS *UMPIRE* WAS A OL' *ROOSTER* AN' WHEN THE *CHICKENS* WANTED TO GIVE A *DANCE* HE SAID IT WOULDN'T BE A *HIT* BECAUSE IT WAS A *FOWL BALL*... "HO HO?"

HE WAS JES' MEAN.

HE WAS A *SPOILSPORT*... PEOPLE LIKE THAT MAKES ME *MAD.*

WELL, AT LEAST IT GOT *SOME* REACTION OUTEN YOU.

NEXT, TO *END THE GAME*, I MOUGHT OF MADE A *OVER-THE-HEAD-GOIN'-AWAY* CATCH OF A SURE *HOMER*.

IT'S A PITY WE DIN'T HAVE A *SCOUT* DOWN FROM THE *BIG LEAGUES!* WITH *ME* PLAYIN' LIKE *THAT* I'D OF BEEN NEXT YEAR'S *BONUS BABY!*

IF YOU *REALLY* WANTS TO GIT INTO A *SPORTS JOB* WHY NOT GO DOWN TO *MIAMI* AN' GIT A JOB AT A *DOG* TRACK?

YOU COULD BE THE FIRST *NON-MECHANICAL RABBIT* IN THE BUSINESS.

UM

THE DOGS *SCARCELY* EVER CATCHES THE RABBIT.

"SCARCELY" GOT A VERY UNPLEASANT RING OF FREQUENCY TO IT.

WULL, MAYBE YOU COULD GET THE *DOGS* CHANGED TO *MECHANICAL DOGS* 'CEPT IT WOULD PUT THE *REAL DOGS* OUTEN BUSINESS.

ANY OTHER ARRANGEMENT WOULD PUT *ME* OUTEN BUSINESS.

CHAPTER

14

Mock the May,

WHAT IN THE *EVER LOVIN'* BLUE-EYED WORLD IS *THAT?*

IT'S MY **SELF-INVENTED** *PRINTIN' PRESS* -- I'SE GOIN' INTO THE BUSINESS OF *PRINTIN' MONEY* ON *FOOD* -- GONNA CORNER THE MARKET.

RIGHT NOW I IS READY TO PRINT A TEN-DOLLAR BILL ON A EGG--

--SAM'WICH

'COURSE MY MACHINE GOT A FEW WRINKLES TO BE IRONED *OUT.*

DON'T YOU FIGGER YOU KIN GIT A-RRESTED FOR PRINTIN' *YO' OWN MONEY?*

'COURSE NOT-- NOBODY EVER BOTHERS THE **GUMMINT** FER DOIN' IT.

BUT THE GUMMINT GOT THE **CONCESSION** -- *EVER'BODY* TAKES OFF'N IT-- IT BEEN PRINTIN' MONEY FOR *YEARS.*

ON *PAPER!*

MY MONEY GONNA BE *TASTY!* IT'LL BE ALL THE RAGE -- JES' IMAGINE, YOU GIVES A FELLA A DOLLAR PRINTED ON A *PANCAKE*--HE GIVES YOU BACK A *HALF A MUSHMELON* IN CHANGE.

FOR *SMALL CHANGE* YOU COULD PRINT PENNIES ON CAVIAR.

NOPE! NOPE! NOTHIN' ILLEGAL ABOUT THIS--- *NO FOREIGN CURRENCIES.*

YOU NOTICE HOW THINGS BEEN GOIN' 'ROUND HERE··? *FIRST* THEY DON'T LAUGH AT OUR JOKES··

NEXT THEY *REE*·FUSE TO PLAY THE *WORLD SERIES,* AS IS OUR WONT, ON ACCOUNT OF HAVIN' *NO BALL* -- AND YOU, BEIN' MY FRIEND, WILL ADMIT WHO WOULD OF BEEN THE STAR IN *THAT*---

SURE.

YOU'RE MY *ONLY* PAL ·· MY ONLY ONLY *ONLY* PAL ·· ··WILLIN' TO ADMIT WHO WOULD OF BEEN *STAR*··

AIN'T NO *TWO* WAYS ABOUT IT·· THE *STAR* WOULD OF BEEN--

---*ME,* YOUR *ONLY* PAL.

HOW'D YOU LIKE A PUNCH IN THE *NOSE,* ONLY PAL?

SUCH AS THEM **REDINGOTES,** YASHMAKS, BEAVERS, KILTS, STOMACHERS, FEDORAS, BURNOOSES, PANTALOONS, KNICKERBOCKERS AND OTHER *IN*-EXPRESSIBLES WITH WHICH YOU IS *MACARONIED-UP.*

IF WE GOES UP THERE **NAKED-BORN** WE'LL COTCH OUR *DEATH!*

'SIDES WE AIN'T HAD THE BORRY OF THEM MORE'N A YEAR.

MM

WELL I WILL BE **HORSE-*REDDISHED***.. YOU'S RETURNIN' MY DUDS!

OOP

AIN'T MORE'N **HALF** OF THESE IS **YOURNS.** I JES' **COMMANDEERED** 'EM BACK FROM ALBERT AN' HOUN'DOG WHICH BORRIED 'EM **TWO** WINTERS AGONE.

IT SO LONG SINCE **YOU** BORRIED THE LOAN OF 'EM MY BEAVER NEED TONSORIAL ATTENTION.

IF **I'D** OF BORRIED 'EM **I'D** OF REE-TURNED 'EM AFORE THIS.

EGG-ZACKLY WHAT I TOLE **THEM** TWO RASCAL BONES.

WELL ~ I'LL BE **HORSE-REDDISHED!**

SAY NO MORE! SAY NO MORE! US PROBBLE BORRIED THEM FROM **YOU** TO WEAR TO MR. COOLIDGE'S **INAUGURIAL BALL.**

I WAS A **DREAM** IN THAT TARBOOSH.

88

WHAT'S THE MATTER WITH OL' **OWL** AN' **CHURCHY**? THEY WALKS UP WITH A BUNCH OF **SMELLY OL' CLOTHES** AN' SAYS THEY'S *MINE*--- THEY NEVER BORRIED 'EM FROM *ME*!

YOO-HOO! COME BACK HERE!

THESE DUDS LOOKS GOOD -- COULD USE 'EM FOR **COWBOY CLO'ES.**

WELL, I'LL JES' GETHER 'EM UP AN' TOSS 'EM IN A HOLE AN' THROW DIRT ON THE **WHOLE SHOOTIN' MATCH.**

YOU DO AN' YOU'S GONE BURY A *MIGHTY FINE LI'L' BOY A-LIVE.*

UNCLE POGO GIVE ME A OL' HAT TO PLAY A LI'L' **SINGLE-HANDED COWBOY** -- **BANG**

WELL, GO OVER AN' **BANG** 'ROUN' HIM --

YOU ALLUS IS **REE-PRESSIN'** MY TALENTS.

THE CHILE'S RIGHT -- *LET HIM BANG!*

15

Rapidly, Vapidly,

WELL, OFF (light hearted) WE GOES.

RIGHT! OH, THIS CROWD HERE WILL BE **SORRY** WHEN WE'RE **GONE.**

THEY WILL NOT **SOON** FORGET THE HAPPY, SUNLIT DAYS WE SPENT TOGETHER--- **AH,** THE **TREASURES** OF OUR **OLD AGE** ARE THE **GOLDEN HOURS** OF OUR **YOUTH** ---THERE WILL BE MANY A **TEAR-STAINED PILLOW** WHEN THEY REALIZE THAT WE----

I'M GOIN' BACK.. I **CAN'T** GO ON.

WHAT IN THE BLUE-EYED WORLD **FOR?**

MY TEDDY BEAR MISSES ME.

HOW CAN YOU CHANGE PLANS NOW AND GO BACK? IT'S **UNTHINKABLE.**

IT IS **NOT.. IT'S THINKABLE ENOUGH.** I THUNK OF IT... I'M GOIN' BACK TO MY **TEDDY BEAR.**

HOW CAN YOUR TEDDY BEAR MISS YOU? **HE** AIN'T **HUMAN.**

HE'S AS HUMAN AS **YOU** IS, FRIEND.

NEXT TO WOMEN AN' CHILLUN, *DOGS* IS THE MOST *HUMAN* OF ALL ANIMALS.

WELL, MY *TEDDY BEAR* BEEN IN MY *EM*-PLOYE LONGER'N *YOU* IS.

HE GOT *SENIORITY* AN' *JUNIORITY* RIGHTS GOIN' BACK TO 19-OUGHT-23.

YO' IS ALLUS BEIN' TURNT BY A *PERTY FACE*...

NOW LET'S SEE···SOMEWHERE HERE IS MY *TEDDY BEAR*···IF I TAKES HIM *WITH* US, HE WON'T BE LONESOME AN' *GRIEF STRICK*·

NOT MEANIN' NO *HARM*, ALBERT OL' *FRIEN'*, BUT···

I NEVER THINK *YOU* WAS THE TYPE TO BE SO *SENTIMENTAL* OVER A OL' *TEDDY BEAR*.

ALBERT

HEE-HEE·· I IS HEERD OF SOME GROWED BOY HERE A BOUTS GOT A *NELLY BOO*···· A YALLER HAIRT, BLUE-EYE-BALLED DOLLY WHAT GO: "*WA-WA*."

THAT'S A *BALL-FACE LIE*.

SNF MY *NELLY BOO* SAY "*DADA*"····· ··SO *SWEET!* "*DA DA*" IS HOW SHE GO···*MSNFF*.

ALBERT

95

WE MUST BE MISSED PERTY BAD BY NOW.

OUR FRIENDS IS PROB'LY CRYIN' THEIR HEARTS OUT... *SOBBIN'* AN'*WEEPIN'...YEARNIN'* FOR OUR RETURN.

TWO SOLID WEEKS OF GRIEF WE IS GRATUITOUSLY GIVE 'EM.

THERE'S OL' PORKY--*LOOKIN'* SAD! POOR PORKY.

PORKYPINE! DON'T *MISS* US SO-- *CHEER UP,* WE'LL *COME BACK!*

COME BACK? YOU BEEN AWAY?

CAN YOU IMAGINE *THAT?* PORKYPINE DIN'T EVEN KNOW WE WAS FIXIN' TO *LEAVE...* AN' I THUNK HE LOOKED SAD ON ACCOUNT WE WAS *GONE.*

HE'S A *PROFESSIONAL* SAD-LOOKER.

HE'S *ALWAYS* SAD-LOOKIN' WHETHER WE IS *LEAVIN'* OR *COMIN'* BACK--

I'VE *NEVER* SEED HIM *HAPPY...* TO GIVE HIM HIS DUE.

MATTER OF FACK HE LOOKED A *TRACE LESS SAD* THIS TIME-- HIS GRIMACE *MOUGHT* OF BEEN A SORTA *CHEAP* SMILE.

I WAS THINKIN' THAT TOO-- YOU FIGGER HE WAS *AMUSED* AT US?

US? THE BEST DRESSED MEN SOUTH OF *WINNIPEGOSIS?* WHAT IMPERTIMINTS OF HIM!

I GOT A GOOD MIND TO TELL HIM OFF-- MAKE HIM *LAUGH ON T'OTHER SIDE OF HIS FACE.*

NINE O'CLOCK AND ALL IS AS WELL AS CAN BE EXPECTED.

HERE I THOUGHT IF WE WENT TO A LOT OF TROUBLE TO *LEAVE* IT WOULD BE APPRECIATED AN'-*WHAT'S THAT?*

IT'S BIG BUN! IT *CAN'T* BE NINE O'CLOCK, BUN.

WHY *CAN'T* IT? WHO'S IN *CHARGE* OF THIS CLOCK?

THE HANDS SAY *THREE O'CLOCK.*

YOU GONNA BELIEVE A PIECE OF OL' McANNICKLE APPARATUMUS OR YOU GONNA BELIEVE *ME,* YOUR FRIEND?

LOOKIN' AT IT LIKE *THIS,* IT SAYS HALF PAST EIGHT.

AN' IT'D TAKE A *HALF HOUR* TO TURN THE CLOCK *UPSIDE DOWN.* BY THEN IT'S *NINE* ON THE NOSE~WHAT *MORE* DO YOU WANT?

HOW'D YOU COME TO BE IN CHARGE OF A GRANDFATHER CLOCK, BUN?

I BOUGHT IT FROM A OL' PARTY WHAT **NEVER RUN IT MUCH**--- HE ONLY LOOKED AT IT ON **CHRISTMAS**.

WAS HE A GRANDFATHER?

NATURALLY-- YOU GOTTA BE A **BONA FRIED GRAN'PA** TO DRIVE ONE OF **THESE** THINGS --STATE LAW YOU KNOW.

DOES YOU MEAN TO SAY **YOU** IS A **GRAN'FATHER**?

WULL --WHEN HE TURNED OVER THE KEYS TO THE CLOCK HE GIVE ME HIS **PEDIGREE**, TOO.

TO BE A GRAN'PA YOU GOTTA HAVE **GRAN'CHILLUN**-- DID THIS FELLA TURN OVER HIS GRAN'CHILLUN AS WELL?

YEP--BUT THEY WAS A **LAZY LOT**--HADN'T MOVED IN **YEARS**--WHEN HE TURNED 'EM OVER **SPIDERS** RUN OUT FROM UNDER SO WE LEFT 'EM BE.

WELL---YOU TOLE US WHAT HAPPENED TO THIS HERE GRAN'PA'S GRAN'CHILLUN BUT HOW 'BOUT GRAN'MA?

SHE EVIDENTLY RUN OFF WITH A **ROCKIN' CHAIR** SALESMAN, NAME OF **LOUIE LOCHINVAR**.

ALL WE HEARD AS THEY RODE OFF IN A **TANDEM ROCKIN' CHAIR** WAS THE PIERCIN' SOPRANO OF GRAN'MA SINGIN' "**OL' LOCHINVAR GOT ME.**"

'TAIN'T NEW, FRIEND.

LOVE IS A *OLD* STORY! ANYWAYS THE GRAN'PA LIVED OUT IN THE CLOCK···· IT WOULD GET MIGHTY *COLD*·· SO THE CHILLUN WOULD INVITE HIM IN FOR MEALS··· ONE EVENIN' ONE SAYS, *"LET'S HAVE COLD GRANDFATHER FOR DINNER."*

"AIN'T YOU EVEN GONNA *WARM HIM OVER?"* I ASKED...SO THAT'S HOW I WON FAVOR AN' HE SOLD ME THE CLOCK WITH A *NINETY-NINE YEAR GUARANTEE*···

ON *YOU* OR THE *CLOCK?*

OORG.

IF THAT **GRANDFATHER** GIVE YOU A GUARANTEE ON THE CLOCK FOR **99 YEAR** HOW COME HE DIDN'T MAKE IT A **EVEN HUNDRED?**

WELL-- THEY'D GAVE THE CLOCK A **TRIAL RUN** AN' **99** WAS *ALL* SHE'D DO-- SO GRAN'PA SAYS, "IF SHE DON'T RUN 99 YEARS FOR YOU COME BACK AN' ·· "

OKEFENOKEE

MR. WILL COX

DANG BLANG IT! IF YOU GONNA TELL SUCH STORIES *WHYN'T YOU GO WHOLE HOG AND SAY A HUNDRED YEARS WHILES YOU'S AT IT?*

AS OL' **UNCLE WILL** WOULD SAY, YOU WOULDN'T WANT ME TO **LIE** FOR JES' **ONE** MEASLY DOG-BONED *YEAR,* WOULD YOU?

THE HON. WILL COX

WAYCROSS

Gimpily, Simpily,

ALL I WAS TRYIN' TO DO WAS MAKE *HAVIN' MONEY* A MORE TASTEFUL TYPE ACTIVITY.

WHAT COULD BE MORE PLEASANT THAN TO REACH INTO YO' *POCKLEBOOK* AN' PULL OUT A FIVE DOLLAR BILL PRINTED ON *LIVERWISHT*? BUT *NO*, THE GUMMINT AIN'T GONE LET *NOBODY* ELSE PRINT MONEY ···

WHY NOT *GIVE* YO' IDEA TO THE *GUMMINT*? THEY'S STORED UP A LOTTA *FOOD·THEY COULD USE THAT.*

MM-- THINK THEY'D PRINT MONEY ON *BUTTER* AN' *EGGS* AN' STUFF?

SURE·- TROUBLE IS WE'D PROB'LY HAVE A SURPLUS AN' HAFTA *BURY* SOME AT *FORT KNOX.*

GREAT! THEREBY CREATIN' A *VAST SALAMI MINE* FOR THE FUTURE.

IF THE GUMMINT *DO* PRINT MONEY ON SURPLUS FOOD MEBBE SOME OF IT'D GIT *ABROAD* AN' SOMEBODY'D GIT *FED.*

PERFECKLY ALLRIGHT FOR *THEM* TO PRINT IT BUT IF *I* TRY IT I'LL GIT LOCKED IN THE *ROCK·HOCKEY HOUSE.*

FOR *HUNDERDS* OF YEARS AS OL' *MAILMAN DUCK* SAID·- AN' THEN *YOU* SAYS I'D BE PRACTICAL *DEAD* WHEN *PENSIONED OFF* —

VIVE ST. CHARLES

102

THERE'S NO FUTURE IN *THAT*.

YOU'D BE *CONDEMNED!* BUT THINK OF ALL THE *HEALTHY BREAKFASTS* THE CONDEMNED MAN--- *(NAMELY YOU)* COULD EAT IN *200 YEARS.*

THAT WOULD BE ROUGHLY *73,000* OF YOUR *FAVORITE TYPE* BREAKFASTS! *FREE!*

73,000 STACKS OF *GRIDDLE CAKES* AN' *SAUSAGES?* A AVERAGE OF *SIX* TO A STACK AN'--*WHOO!* I'D BE *WORKIN'* MY WAY THRU *JAIL!*

VIVE ST. CHARLES

H'LO THERE, UNCLE POGO, AN' H'LO THERE, *GRUNDOON,* I AIN'T SEEN YOU SINCE PA DECIDED HE COULDN'T *AFFORD* TO *RUN AWAY* FROM *HOME* 'CAUSE WE ALL WANTED TO GO *WITH* HIM, IS I?

NOPE

GNX

WELL--HOW'S THINGS WITH YOU, GRUNDOON? KEEPIN' *BUSY?*

ZMNX KPSTVWN RQFSBD NP NP NP *NP!*

WHITE HOPES and

NP!? GOSH, WODDYA THINK OF *THAT,* UNCLE POGO?

NOT MUCH--AN' *NEITHER DO YOU* YOU KNOW OL' GRUNDOON'S TALK *DON'T MAKE SENSE.*

WULL--WHAT OF IT--? *HE'S* NO DIFFER'NT *ANYBODY ELSE*--HE'S JES' INNERESTED IN *TALKIN'*---MAKIN' SENSE IS A ENTIRELY DIFFER'NT TALENT.

WHITE HOPES AND OT TIG

WHAT'S YOU USIN' FOR BAIT, UNCLE POGO?

THE USUAL, CAVIAR, BONBONS, CHAMPAGNE AND MINK.

BEST BAIT I IS FOUND FOR *SURE KETCHIN'* IS GRUNDOON.

GRUNDOON?

YEP, YOU GITS HIM BY THE *PANTS* AN' HANG HIM DOWN NEAR THE WATER··· *HE MAKES A NOISE LIKE A FISH*··· ONE SURFACES AN' *SNAP!*

GRS GRS

SNAP? MY SAKES! DO THE FISHES *BITE HIM* AN' YOU HAULS 'EM IN?

NOPE-*HE* BITES THE FISH AN' WE HAULS 'EM IN···· ONLY TROUBLE IS IT'S KINDA HARD MAKIN' HIM LET GO.

GRS

I *SWEAR* THAT TURTLE GITS *BRAIN*LESSER AND *BRAIN*-LESSER EVERY DAY.

DON'T SWEAR 'N FRONT THE CHILDER.

RIGHT

GRS

I *WASN'T* SWEARIN'·· WHAT'S YOU *DOIN'*?

YOU WAS TOO··YOU *SAID* SO.

I WAS *NOT* -- I TAKES MY OATH THAT I -

YOU AIN'T GONE USE NO OATH IN FRONT OF *THESE* INNOCEMENT EARS -- TEACHIN' *BAD WORDS!*

HOW 'BOUT *MY* EARS? I IS DELICATE.

HOW COULD I TEACH *GRUNDOON* BAD WORDS? -- HE DON'T KNOW ANY *GOOD* ONES -- HE CAN'T TALK.

HE TALKS TO FISHES --- YOU WANT *THEM* CURSIN' AN' CARRYIN' ON?

YEH --- FISH GOT CHILLUN TOO.

HOW CAN YOU SAY GRUNDOON TALKS TO *FISH*?! HE CAN'T TALK *A-TALL.*

I TAKES THE WORD OF THE *CHILE* EXPERT HERE, *RACKETY COON CHILE,* ON ACCOUNT HE'S A EXPERT CHILE HISSELF.

RIGHT

ALL RIGHT, PROFESSOR, WHAT KINDA OF A NOISE DOES GRUNDOON *THINK* FISHES MAKES?

LISTEN

GRS

DO YOU TAKE ME FOR A *NINCOMPOST?* "GRS" HA! -- INDEED! IMAGINE A FISH RESPONDING TO *GRS!*

GRS!

CHAPTER

18

Crow the Cry,

HOME!! a masterpiece OF NAVIGATION ALL THE WAY TO THE SWEET SUWANNEE'S SOURCE FROM JERSEY CITY, LILY OF the GARDEN STATE.!!

WHAT WILL I DO WITH THE PUMPED-UP SEA HORSE, O MINE CRISTOBAL?

LEAVE IT BE!

LEAVE IT BE? IT'S GOT NINE HUNDERD CUBIC POUNDS OF MY PERSONAL BREATHIN' IN IT— DON'T I EVEN GET MY BREATH BACK?

COME along.. COME A-LONG!

DRAGONS, MERMAINS, PIXLES, ELFS AND SEA SERPENTS ARE ALL NON-EXISTENT, JEROME, AS YOUR GRAMPA ALLUS SAID AN'—

YEH YEH YEP

AACK! YOU LEGENDARY LUNKHEAD! YOU'VE DESTROYED THE FAITH OF A SON IN BOTH OUR FATHERS!

HEY! HEY! HEY! DROP EVERYTHING! I GOT A SPECIAL DIS-PATCH FLASHED HERE FROM P.T. BRIDGEPORT AN' TAMMANANNY WHAT WENT UP TO RADIO CITY TO SEEK THEIR FORTUNES IN THE TEEVIES!

Z ZZ

COME ON! DROP WHAT YOU IS DOIN'— THAT KIN KEEP.... THIS HERE'S A SPECIAL DEE-LIVERARY MESSAGE FROM TWO IM-PORTANT PEOPLE...

ZZZZ!

Dimpily, Limpily,

I SAYS IS IT *OKAY* DO I LEAVE ON MY HAT AN' ALL I GET IS A *BLANK-EYE-BALLED STARE* --- YOU COULD LEARN A FEW MANNERS..

HERE; HOLE THE HAT WHILST I CRAWDADS AROUN' ON MY BACK... *LEASTWISE* YOU AIN'T A *JABBY-WOCKER* LIKE THAT *RABBIT* --- *HE* MUST OF WAS BORNED ON THE TOP FLOOR OF A *PHONO-GRAFT!*

MAN! HE TOLE US ALL 'BOUT *HOW* COME HE'S IN CHARGE OF A *GRAN'-FATHER CLOCK* --- HE TOLE US 'BOUT A *CHICKEN* WHAT HE WAS *LAID OFF* FROM THE *EASTER BUSINESS* WITH, ONCE --- HE TOLE HOW HE HAD A OFFER TO GO INTO THE *LUCKY RABBIT FOOT* GAME --- BUT WAS AFEARED IT'D LEAVE HIM *SHORT-HANDED* -- WHOO, I'M GLAD *YOU* AIN'T NO TALKER.

HOWEVER, WHAT IS YOU *INSINUATIN'* BY BEIN' SO *DOGBONED CLOSEMOUTHED?*

IF YOU IS GONE HAVE A IMPERTIMENT ATTITUDE SUCH AS A: KEEPIN' YO' *THOUGHTS* TO YO'SELF, AN' B: BEIN' STAREY-EYED --

YOU CAN C: *GIMME BACK MY HAT!*

SMOOP

IS YOU FIGHTIN' OR KISSIN'?

YO' QUIET DEE-MEANOR DEMEANS OUR ACQUAINTANCESHIP--UNDER BENEATH YOU IS PLOTTIN' SOME KIND OF INSCRUTABOBBLE ORIENTAL LOW JINX.

YOU KIN SMILE AN' SMILE AN' YET BE A VILLAIN.

RUN OUT ON ME!

COMMUNIST! YOU PUT OUT MY SEE-GAR.

114

DOGGONE! THE *RIGORS* OF YO' *MORTIS* IS THROWED A SNEAK PUNCH AFTER THE *BELL--*

ALBERT! YOU LOOKS PUZZLED-- MEBBE MY FRESH YOUNG BRAIN KIN HELP ON ACCOUNT I AIN'T USED IT TODAY.

I GOT A *RIGOR MORTAL* OVER THERE WHAT'S *DEE-FYIN'* HIS OWN FUNERAL.

MY WORD-- HE'S A *FLAT* ONE-- HOW'D HE GIT LIKE *THAT?*

WE WAS HAVIN' A LI'L CONTEST OF SKILL AN' HE SUDDEN *EXPIRED.*

PHOOMPH-- YO' FRIEND AIN'T REAL *ALIVE* NO-HOW.

I *KNOWS* THAT-- HE PASSED ON *UN-EXPECTED* DURIN' THE FRACAS-- BUT HE'S STILL PERTY *TRICKY.*

THIS HERE'S NOTHIN' BUT ONE OF THEM *RUBBER BEACH HORSES!*

BY JING, IT'S GITTIN' SO A MAN CAN'T EVEN DEPEND ON HIS *ENEMIES.*

CHAPTER

20

Do.

FUNNY THING, ME AN' ALBERT WAS **THINKIN'** OF GOIN' TO NEW YORK FOR NEARLY THREE WEEKS **AN' NOT A SOUL MISSED US...**

HERE I AN' **P.T.** IS OFF IN **JERSEY CITY** FOR MONTHS AN' NARY ONE "HELLO!".. NOT A "WELCOME HOME." HAWGH!

TAMMANANNY! OL' *TIGER*!

HOUN'DOG! YOU OL' BEAUREGARD YOU!

BY **NEDDIE DINGO**! **IT'S GOOD TO SEE YOU!**

AND YOU! A SIGHT FOR SORE EYES!

I'M GLAD I'M BACK!

I'M GLAD I'M BACK!

YOU WAS AWAY?

IT SURE IS DISCOURAGIN' TO GO ABROAD AN' DON'T HAVE **NOBODY** DO NIP-UPS ON ONE'S RETURN.

I COULD OF SWORE YOU'D ALL BE OUT TO SHOUT, "*WELL DONE!*" WHEN WE RETURNED...

IT SEEMED TO ME THERE MIGHT BE A **PARADE**···· LIKE WHEN HEROES RETURN TO LOWER BROADWAY THEY GITS A TICKER TAPE SHOWER!···· BANDS PLAY···· BEAUTIFUL GIRLS THROW ROSES ···· MAYORS GREET··

···NOT **EVERYBODY** GOES OFF TO SEEK HIS FORTUNE·· NOT **EVERYBODY** HAS THE **HEART**··NOT **EVERYBODY** COMES BACK COVERED WITH GLORY, HONOR AND THE LOVE OF A GREAT PUBLIC··

IF WE'D ONLY **KNOWED**.

YES ··· LIKE I SAY, NOT **EVERYBODY** COMES BACK COVERED WITH GLORY, HONOR AND THE LOVE OF A GREAT PUBLIC ····BUT 'LEAST WE'RE **BACK**.

SOME DON'T GIT **THAT** FAR.

SOME PEOPLE GITS **ALL** THE BREAKS····YOU AN' P.T. GITS TO TRAVEL TO THE **BIG TOWN** AN' BECOMES INVOLVED IN **SUCCESS**.

SUCCESS··THE GILDED GODDESS WAS **YOURS**·· YOURS IN A **EN-CHANTED LAND** OF LOTUS AN' LACE.

SUCCESS?! ANYBODY CAN GET AS FAR AS **JERSEY CITY** WHICH WAS AS FAR AS WE WENT··· NO ENCHANTMENT TO SPEAK OF.

WELL, AT LEAST YOU STRUCK OUT ON YOUR OWN.

WE STRUCK OUT ALL RIGHT·· WE DIN'T EVEN GIT A MAN ON FIRST BASE.

WHAT I MEANS YOU HAD THE GUMPTION AT LEAST TO BE ANYWAYS A **FAILURE** ···MOST OF US NEVER EVEN TRIES FER **THAT**.

DOGGONE! IF YOU WANNA BE A **FAILURE**, I CAN SHOW YOU HOW TO DO IT IN ONE EASY LESSON IN YO' **SPARE TIME**.

AS FER ME I FAIL TO SEE THE NECESSITY OF TRAVELIN' FAR AFIELD IN SEARCH OF OPPORTUNITY.

YOU MEAN YOU CAN GET THE CHANCE TO FLOP AT HOME AS WELL AS ABROAD?

IT'S ALL ACCORDIN' TO HOW YOU LOOK AT IT -- TAKE COUSIN EARS -- HE TOOK A JOB AS A HEARING AIDE -- SORT OF A VICE PRESIDENT TO A HARD OF HEARING GENERAL.

ONE DAY THE GENERAL CALLS IN EARS AN' SAYS: "SERGEANT, I'M WORRIED." AN' COUSIN EARS SHOUTS: "HOW CAN YOU BE? I NEVER TELL YOU ANYTHING THAT'LL WORRY YOU EVEN IF I HEAR IT."

"THAT'S WHAT WORRIES ME!" CRIED THE GENERAL, "HOW CAN I TELL IF THE ENEMY'S ON MY TRAIL?" "EASY" SCREAMED EARS, "YOU'LL SEE ME RUNNIN' AHEAD OF YOU WITHOUT WAITIN' FOR INSTRUCTIONS." STRANGELY, WE NEVER HEARD OF HIM AGAIN.

WHEN YOU AN' P.T. LEFT FOR THE BIG CITY WHAT LINE WAS YOU GOIN' INTO?

INTO TEEVY! WE DECIDED SHOW BUSINESS WAS DEAD AN' TO GIT INTO A EN-TIRELY DIFFERNT FIELD.

AH, YES.. THE LINE WHERE THEY ASKS YOU QUESTIONS AN' PAYS YOU BIG MONEY.

YEP -- I WAS ALL GROOMED FOR THE $63,999.99 QUESTION PROGRAM

$63,999.99 QUESTION PROGRAM? A ODD SUM.

YES.... IT WAS A **LOW** BUDGET SHOW---- ----THEY KNOCKED A LITTLE OFF.

WELL, I ARRIVED AN' SAID, "I HAVE A *$63,999.99 ANSWER* FOR YOU!" "WHAT IS IT?" THEY INQUIRED. "THE ANSWER" I SAID CALMLY "IS NORTH DAKOTA IN THE YEAR 1822." "SPLENDID" SCREAMED A QUIET CHAP, "BUT WE HAVE NO **QUESTION** FOR THAT **ANSWER**." WELL, I'D DONE *MY PART* SO I PHONED THE POLICE AND ---

NOT MEANIN' TO BE NOSEY BUT **WHAT** KIND OF A QUESTION WOULD YOUR ANSWER *"NORTH DAKOTA IN 1822"* HAVE FITTED?

SHUCKS! THAT WASN'T **MY** JOB I WASN'T IN CHARGE OF THE **TEEVY** PROGRAM.

OL' LOU COWAN

BY GEORGE, IF **THEY** DIDN'T HAVE A **QUESTION** TO FIT THE ANSWER **THAT** WASN'T MY LOOKOUT.

I KNOWED A FELLOW OVER IN **AUGUSTA** WHAT GOT HOME TIRED IN THE AFTERNOON AN' SAT *LOOKIN' OUT THE WINDOW* FOR TWO HOURS FIGURIN' IT WAS A *TELEVISION SET*---

THE HON. MR. LOU C.

HIS WIFE LOOKED IN THE WINDOW TO SEE IF HE WAS HOME -- AN' WHEN SHE ENTERED, HE HOLLERED: "GERT, I SEEN YOU ON THE TEEVIES, BUT YOU COME IN *UGLY*." "AN' *THAT'S* THE WAY YOU'RE GOIN' OUT," SHE SAID, AN'.....

HO HUM

122

Hoppingly, Stoppingly,

HOW **GOOD** OF YOU TO TURN OUT TO WELCOME US BACK TO OUR **NATIVE SOIL**··· WE, WHO DISCOVERED AMERICA···*HUZZAH*, MR. PRESIDENT.

BUT·· I ····UH· ···YOU·· NOBODY **HERE** IS PRESIDENT ··UH··· YOU MUST OF GOT **OFF** AT THE **WRONG STOP.**

HO HO! *THANK YOU FOR THAT MODEST SPEECH OF WELCOME*··· IT IS GOOD TO SEE THAT THIS LAND WHICH **WE** DISCOVERED SO MANY YEARS AGO WAS LEFT IN SUCH **GOOD HANDS.**

YOUR **STEWARDSHIP** WAS WELL DISCHARGED! BOTH OF YOU MAY SIT DOWN··· I'LL ISSUE YOU A **PERMIT** TO GO ON **BREATHING** IN THE MORNING·· *HA HA* TO ALL··

YOU SAID IT.

THE MINUTE I HEARD YOU WERE ELECTED **PRESIDENT**, MR. POSSUM, I SAID TO MY **CRUSTY·CRESTED COCKADOO** HERE, I SAID, "LET'S GO SEE HIM **BEFORE** HE INVITES US! HE'LL BE TICKLED TO DEATH."

POLLY WANT A CRACKER?

MY NAME AIN'T POLLY.

BUT I AIN'T **PRESIDENT**·· ALL'S WE HAD WAS **NOMINATION** CONVENTIONS.

YES···YES, **YOUR SYSTEM** HAS A FEW **HOLES** IN IT, BUT WE CAN **FIX** THAT.

·YOU SAID IT.

126

128

CHAPTER

22

Stow the Stew,

UNLESS I *WEIGHS* THIS LETTER AN' MEASURES HOW FAR I BRUNG IT, THE POSTAGE-DUE CAN'T BE PAID.

A *EXCELLENT* ARRANGEMENT.

THE GUMMINT GOT A NOBLE WAY ON 'EM.

AN' UNLESS YOU *PAYS* IT···· YOU DON'T GIT TO *READ* THE LETTER.

LIKE WE SAID, THE GUMMINT IS A *PACK* OF *THIEVES.*

ALSO, I *FLEW* A LITTLE ON THE WAY··· THERE'S *AIR MAIL* ADDED RIGHT *THERE!*

YOU WEREN'T UP IN THE AIR ALL THE WAY WERE YOU? THIS THING'S BEEN A LONG TIME ON THE WAY.

HOW ABOUT IF I *READS* IT TO YOU FOR A *REDUCED RATE?*

NOTHIN' DOIN'···· IT MAY BE *VERY SECRET.*

LET HIM GO AHEAD. IT'S *PROB'LY NOT IN ENGLISH* AN' *HE* WON'T UNDERSTAND A WORD OF IT.

IF YOU DON'T TELL ME *WHERE* THIS IS FROM SO'S I KIN GIVE YOU A *RATE* ON IT··· IT'S GONNA BE *HARD* TO READ THIS.

·IF IT'S FROM WHERE I *THINK,* IT'S GONNA BE *IMPOSSIBLE* TO READ IT.

I GOTTA FIGURE *HOW FAR* I IS CARRIED THIS···· THEN, I READS IT AT *SO MUCH* PER WORD.

SOME OF THEM WORDS IN THERE IS BOUND TO BE PERTY *CHEAP.*

HOW KIN YOU SAY I IS THE **COMMON ENEMY?** CAN'T YOU TALK NICER ABOUT A **OLD COMRADE?**

I *COULD* SAY YOU IS AN **UNUSUALLY COMMON** ENEMY.

WELL.. *THAT'S BETTER*.... IT SHOWS YOU STILL CARES.

EVEN IF YOU IS OUR COMMON ENEMY, I IS *STILL* YOUR BEST FRIEND.

AN' **THAT** GOES FOR ME...THO' I IS **YOUR** ENEMY, WE IS BONDED BY THE **BOUNDS** OF FRIENDSHIP.

RIGHT! WE IS FELLOW BOUNDERS.

HEY! I BEEN HOLDIN' YO' LETTER EVERY-WINCH-WAY AN' IT **STILL** LOOKS UPSIDE-DOWN.. IT'S THE ONLY LETTER I EVER SAW WHAT'S GOT *TWO UPSIDE-DOWN* SIDES.

IT'S FROM THE BOSS!

I'LL READ THIS LETTER **THREE YEARS** OVERDUE FROM THE BOSS.... "YOU DECODE AS I GO, "DEAR CONFRERES: WELL, HERE IT IS MAY AND APRIL. WE ARE HAVING A **BACKWARD** SEASON.

"WE ARE THINKING OF SELLING MOTHER TO A CIRCUS AND DADDY SAYS THIS IS UNFAIR. HE MEANS UNFAIR TO THE CIRCUS"....

SO FAR THE CODE SAYS... *"DESTROY!"*

"AUNT MOOBLE HAS RUN OFF WITH 400 POUNDS OF KNOCK-WURST AND THE MILKMAN."...THERE...I'M HALFWAY THRU. WHAT'S IT SAY UP TO NOW?

IT SAYS: "DESTROY THIS BEFORE READING FURTHER."

I'M MAD! THEM COWBIRDS GOT A LETTER FULL OF CODE.

AIN'T THAT THEIR PRIVILEGE?

MOUGHT EVEN OF BEEN A FOREIGN CODE!

WELL... WHY NOT? IT WAS THEIR LETTER.

BUT SUPPOSE IT WAS SPY SECRETS AN' STUFF---- -- I WOULD BE RESPONSIBLE. ME, THE MAIL MAN---- I DELIVERED IT!

WHAT OF IT? YOU DIN'T KNOW WHAT WAS IN IT.

THAT'S WHAT BURNS MY TIME!

135

NO SECRET WHAT'S WORTH A HOOT OUGHT TO BE KEPT QUIET.

SECRETS IS *USUALLY* PERTY DOGGONE FASCINATIN'.

EGG-*ZACKLY*---- IT'S COMPLETELY *ILLOGICAL* TO KEEP A SECRET SECRET.

AN' UNFAIR.

I THINK I'LL GIT INTO SOME OTHER LINE OF **COMMUNICATION**---- IT AIN'T AS MUCH **FUN** BEIN' A MAILMAN AS IT **USED**.

HOW 'BOUT HOG CALLIN'?

NO---NO--- YOU CALL A HOG AN' *WHERE'S* IT GET YOU? EVEN IF HE *ANSWERS* ---WHAT'RE YOU GONNA *TALK* ABOUT?

IT'S ALL ACCORDIN' TO **WHAT** YOU CALL HIM.

IT AIN'T THAT I DON'T LIKE **MAILMANNIN'**---- BUT THE ZING GOES OUT OF IT WHEN EVER'BODY PUTS STUFF IN **ENVELOPES**. IT'S SNEAKY.

YOU PREFERS **POST CARDS**?

YOU'RE **DERN TOOTLE!** GIVE A MAN A DECK OF **POST CARDS** TO DELIVER AN' HE'S GOT A BUSY, HAPPY DAY AHEAD OF HIM, READIN' AN' CHUCKLIN'--- BUT NOWADAYS PROSPERITY GOT EVER'BODY MAILIN' STUFF THE *EXPENSIVE* WAY.

GOOD TIMES IS BAD?

WHAT HAPPENED TO MR. PIG AND HIS TALKY COCKADOODLE?

YOU INSULTED HIM AND HE UP AN' LEFT.

I *NEVER*--- I TOLE THE TRUTH---I CALLED HIM A BUM----

AN' YOU TALKED LIKE YOU WAS GONNA PUNCH HIM IN THE NOSE.

YOU FIGGER THAT MR. PIG IS *IGNORIN'* US?

BUT YOU *CHASED* HIM OFF.

I AND YOU WAS *RIZ* WITH THE CODE OF THE GENNLEMAN *BURNED* INTO OUR BABY BRAINS---- IT AIN'T *POLITE* TO NOT COME CALLIN' TO PAY YO' RESPECTS.

"GIT AWAY!" IS WHAT YOU TOLE HIM---

AN' *GIT AWAY* IS WHAT HE IS DOOD.

HE'S *DEE*-LIBERATE SNUBBIN' OF US.

BY JING--HE BETTER NOT SHOW UP AROUN' HERE WITHOUT *FIRST* COMIN' BACK AN' PAYIN' HIS *REE*-SPECTS.

CHAPTER

23

Moppily, Sloppily,

IF ONLY WE'D OF *NOT* BURNED THAT LETTER AND *READ* IT INSTEAD.

BUT IT *SAID* TO DESTROY IT *BEFORE* WE READ IT··· WE *READ* THAT MUCH OF IT···

THEN WE BETTER KEEP IT QUIET··· IF WE WERE SUPPOSED TO DESTROY IT *BEFORE WE READ IT*···

-- WE SHOULDN'T HAVE READ *ANY* OF IT··· KEEP IT A *SECRET* OR WE'LL BE IN TROUBLE···

YEAH··· SHHH

WHAT WE'VE GOT TO DO IS KEEP QUIET ABOUT THE FACT WE READ AS MUCH OF THE LETTER AS WE DID.

RIGHT. KEEP QUIET.

I *AM* KEEPIN' QUIET··· I'M NOT TELLIN' ANYBODY···I'M *QUIET!*

IT MIGHT BE FATAL TO TELL 'EM THAT WE READ ANY PART.

140

141

IT'S A GOOD THING I PAID A VISIT TO THE **COUNTRY** WHICH **I** DISCOVERED·· ··JUST TO CHECK UP ON WHAT **YOU TWO** ARE UP TO····

WE GOT YOUR LETTER AND DID LIKE YOU SAID.

YOU ALSO WERE TRYING TO TELL THE **SECRET** TO YOUR COMRADE·· ····*A DANGEROUS PRACTICE!*

YOU SAID IT.

YES, A **VERY** DANGEROUS THING TO DO···· SECRETS ARE **NOT** TO BE TOLD.

YOU SAID IT.

I WAS LOYAL! I DIDN'T **LISTEN** TO HIM.

AND THAT'S EVEN WORSE! SECRETS ARE NOT MEANT TO BE **TOLD** BUT THEY **ARE** MEANT TO BE LISTENED TO··· YOU **BOTH** HAVE FAILED IN YOUR DUTY.

THE **INSTRUCTIONS** IN THE LETTER WERE PRETTY **PLAIN,** I TRUST?

YOU SAID IT.

YOU SAID IT.

YOU SAID IT.

WHAT DID YOU THINK OF DIRECTIVE NO. 2?

WELL, MOSTLY IT WAS **HARD TO READ.**

HARD TO READ?! IT WAS JUST AS CLEAR AS **NO. 1**, WASN'T IT?

MAYBE-- BUT NO.1 SAID TO *DESTROY* THE LETTER BEFORE READING ANY FURTHER.

WELL--- YES, THAT *MIGHT* HAVE MADE NO.2 HARD TO READ, AT THAT.

HE SAID IT.

IT BURNED NICE, ANYWAY.

COME ON-- 'LONG AS YOU'RE VISITIN' US WE'LL TAKE YOU TO A *GOOD* PLACE TO *EAT.*

EXCELLENT! BUT I STILL CAN'T SEE WHY YOU DIDN'T READ *MORE* OF THAT LETTER.

BUT YOUR *VERY* FIRST INSTRUCTION TOLD US TO DESTROY THE LETTER---

--*BEFORE* READING ANY FURTHER.

BUT, BESIDES FOLLOWING OUT DIRECTIONS, YOUR DUTIES ALSO ARE TO *PRY* AND *SNOOP.*

YOU SAID IT.

MM, THE FOOD *IS* GOOD! WHAT LED YOU TO COME *HERE?*

WELL, THE DOOR WAS OPEN.

POGO

145

146

CHAPTER

24

Fry.

WHAT'S THAT OL' MR. PIG *WANT*?

WULL, HE SAYS HE KIN CHANGE OUR ELECTION WAYS--- HE CLAIM WE IS OUTDATED.

OL' DAVE BRINKLEY

HE SAY OUR *WINNIN'* CANDIDATES DON'T GIT ENOUGH OF THE VOTE --- SAYS HE KNOWS A WAY TO GIT 95% OF IT.

MARSE BRINKLEY

WULL --- WHAT'S WRONG WITH *THAT*?

THE WAY HE DO IT--- YOU JES' PUT UP *ONE* CANDIDATE--- CONSEQUENTLY, MOST EVER'BODY'S *FOR* HIM --- THEY'S NOBODY TO BE AGAINST.

OH, *THAT'D* NEVER WORK HERE --- I *USUAL* VOTES 95% *AGAINST* SOMEBODY. HOW COULD I VOTE IF I DIN'T HAVE NOBODY TO BE AGAINST?

YOU COULD WRITE IN YO' *OWN* NAME.

UNCLE DAVE BRINKLEY

THE TROUBLE WITH *YOU* IS YOU GOT *TOO MANY* CAMPAIGN MANAGERS --- I'M GONNA TAKE OVER AN' *SETTLE* THIS.

FER 'NINSTANCE, THERE'S *OWL*, AN' *P.T. BRIDGEPORT* AN' THE *TURTLE* AN' OL' *HOUN'DOG* AN' NOW THIS *MR. PIG*, WHO ADDS *HIS* TWO-CENTS WORTH.

FIRST PIECE OF ADVICE I GIVES YOU, AS YOUR CAMPAIGN MANAGER, IS *GET RID OF ALL YOUR CAMPAIGN MANAGERS!*

ALL OF 'EM?

GOOD ADVICE! IT'S TOO BAD TO HAFTA GET RID OF YOU SO SOON, BUT I VALUES YOUR HELP TOO MUCH TO GO COUNTER TO YO' ADVICE, SO GOODBYE.

SEEM LIKE I HANDLED THIS WRONG, SOMEHOW.

SOMETIMES I *GOTTA* ADMIT I *DOESN'T* UNDERSTAND YOU, POGO.

THAT MAKES US *EVEN*--- I DON'T UNDERSTAND MYSELF SOMETIMES TOO.

HMM---*THAT'S* QUEER---I *ALLUS* UNDERSTANDS MY-SELF---'CEPT WHEN I IS *MAD* AT MYSELF AN' ISN'T *SPEAKIN'* TO ME.

THE AMERICAN HERITAGE

BUT *YOU!* I DON'T KNOW WHY YOU AIN'T OUT *CAM-PAIGNIN'* AN' *COUNTER-PAIGNIN'*.

'CAUSE I'M GONE DO THE ONLY GOOD THING A POSSUM KIN DO---I'M GONNA *VOTE.*

LEASTWISE YOU'LL *VOTE* FOR YO' *OWN SELF*---

I DUNNO--- I'M GONE LOOK OVER *ALL* THE CANDIDATES AN' VOTE FOR WHO I THINKS IS BEST---

THE AMERICAN HERITAGE

VOTE KIDS

FIRST YOU **STUMPS** THE COUNTRY-- NEXT YOU **STUMPS** *ME!*

ANYWAY, IT WOULDN'T BE *RIGHT* FER ME TO VOTE FER MYSELF.

WHY NOT!? EVER'BODY ELSE DOES!

WELL--- WHEN I STOPS AN' *THINKS* OF IT--- I AIN'T **OLD ENOUGH.**

DID I HEAR YOU RIGHT? YOU **AIN'T OLD ENOUGH** TO VOTE?

YUP.

WHAT A *BLOW!* THAT MEANS YOU AIN'T OLD ENOUGH TO BE PRESIDENT, NEITHER.

RIGHT.

WELL! WELL! IT LOOKS LIKE I'LL GOTTA OFFER *MY* FAIR YOUNG BODY IN YOUR *STEAD--- -- I* WILL RUN FOR PRESIDENT.

YOU!? YOU AIN'T ANY OLDER'N *ME!*

BUT *I'M* WILLING TO *LIE* FOR MY COUNTRY!

CHAPTER

25

Startedly, **H***eartedly,*

IF WE MAKE A NEW ORIGINAL PLAN-- IT MEANS WE WON'T BE AS FRIENDLY THIS TIME. RIGHT?

WE'LL BE *MAD.*

MAYBE THEY'LL BE *EXPECTING* US TO SWITCH--- WE'LL HAVE TO *OUTWIT* THEM.

SO WE'LL NOT *SWITCH.* WE'LL BE FRIENDLY! WE'LL SMILE.

BUT THEY MIGHT FIGURE WE WON'T SWITCH-- THEY'RE PRETTY SHARP.

THEN WE'LL THINK *PAST* THEM--- WE'LL SWITCH BACK TO SWITCHING--- THAT'LL FOOL THEM.

NOT *TOO* FAST--- S'POSE THEY FIGURE WE'LL SWITCH BACK TO SWITCHING, SO WE'LL SWITCH BACK FROM SWITCHING TO *NOT SWITCHING.*

GOOD-- NOW DOES THAT LEAVE US BEING FRIENDLY OR *UNFRIENDLY?*

YOU SAID IT.

THE NEW ORIGINAL PLAN WILL BE FOR US TO BE *FRIENDLY* BUT FIRM--- WE WANT TO HELP THESE PEOPLE.

YOU SAID IT.

THE COMING ELECTION IN THIS COUNTRY IS BEING HELD IN A *VERY* OLD-FASHIONED WAY!--IMAGINE, TWO MAJOR CANDIDATES!

YOU SAID IT.

WE DO THINGS MUCH BETTER IN **OUR** COUNTRY·· JUST **ONE** CANDIDATE···· IT **SIMPLIFIES** THE ELECTION··· NOBODY IS IN DOUBT AS TO **WHO** TO VOTE FOR.

YOU SAID IT.

WHY NOT JUST **APPOINT** THE MAN··· AND DO AWAY WITH THE ELECTION?

WHAT? AND **CRUDELY** ABANDON THE SACRED PRINCIPLES OF **TRUE DEMOCRACY?!**

SHAME ON YOU.

YOU SAID IT.

IT'S OUR **DUTY** TO ADVISE THESE PEOPLE THAT **TWO** CANDIDATES ARE CONFUSING.

YOU SAID IT.

EVEN **ONE** CANDIDATE CAN BE CONFUSING.

NOW LET'S NOT BE SO FACETIOUS··· YOU NEED AT **LEAST ONE** CANDIDATE IN AN ELECTION··· **BUT**, WHY USE **MORE?** ONLY **ONE MAN** GETS ELECTED.

YOU SAID IT.

WHY USE **TWO MEN** TO RUN FOR OFFICE WHEN **ONE** WILL DO?···· IT'S A WASTE OF **MANPOWER**; IT **SAPS** THE COUNTRY'S STRENGTH.

YOU SAID IT.

SURE, WHY TIE UP **TWO GOOD MEN?**

TUT! ACROSS THE SEA IN **OUR** COUNTRY WE **KNOW** THERE IS JUST **ONE** GOOD MAN··· AND HE'S THE ONE WE RUN FOR OFFICE··· IN THAT WAY WE MAKE IT **EASY** FOR THE VOTERS··· THEY DON'T EVEN HAVE TO **THINK**.

YOU SAID IT.

155

CHAPTER

26

See the Sea,

159

NOW YOU HAVE DID IT! YOU'VE BLOWED THE SATELLITE UP AN' AROUND THE WORLD.

I NEVER!

POGO WAS HERE~ WHERE'S HE NOW?

WULL~ I HEARD A *VOICE* INSIDE THE GARBAGE CAN.

THAT WAS *HIM!* NOW HE'S *UP* THERE CIRCLING THE EARTH EVERY NINETY MINUTES ON THE HOUR.

GOSH! WHAT'LL I DO *NOW?*

YOU *MIGHT* TAKE OFF YO' HAT AN' GIT *READY* TO *WAVE* --- THE BOY'S ABOUT DUE BY---

162

CHAPTER

27

Markedly, Starkedly,

165

166

167

CHAPTER

28

Bray.

170

Knitfully, Knackfully,

177

YOU'VE DONE YOURSELF PROUD, COBBER····THE *EARTH* IS PROUD, MARS WILL BE PROUD····*I'M* PROUD.

POGO'S THE *CHAMP*····HE TOOK LONGER'N ANYBODY TO DO THE PEN-TATHLON····AND DIN'T EVEN FINISH.

AT *THAT RATE*; I SHOULD BE CHAMPION····I DIDN'T SO MUCH AS MAKE A BLOOMIN' START.

HERE'S YOUR DOGGONE *BOOMERANG* BACK···· I THOUGHT THESE THINGS WAS SUPPOSED TO *RETURN* OF THEIR OWN ACCORD?

THE *DINKUM OIL* IS, COBBER, THAT YOU OFTEN MUST GO OUT AND *PERSUADE* THE JOKERS A BIT.

HERE'S TO RUDDY OL' MARS, OUR SISTER' BLINKIN' PLANET!

CHAPTER

30

Know the Nay,

YOU SAY YOU CAME DOWN TO AUSTRALIA ON A ELKS CONVENTION, UNCLE ANTLER?

YEP, BUT ALL I FOUND WAS A BUNCH OF GUYS RUNNIN' AROUND IN THEIR UNDERWEARS.

THEY SAID IT WAS THE OLYMPIC GAMES, BUT I THINK THEY WAS LOONEY BIN BAIT.

SO I GOT A JOB AS A NIGHT WATCHMAN AT A DAIRY FARM, BUT THERE WASN'T MUCH TO WATCH.

AND I DIDN'T MIND WHEN ONE FELLOW CALLED ME A COW, BUT WHEN ANOTHER COME AT ME WITH A MILK PAIL I DECIDED TO CLIMB THE FENCE AND HEAD FOR HOME.

IF YOU WANT TO GO BACK HOME, COME ALONG WITH ME.

SURE, HOW YOU GOIN'?

WELL, A FELLOW IN A RED SUIT, WEARIN' A WHITE BEARD, IS IN TOWN WITH A REINDEER GROUP.

THAT SOUNDS LIKE...

SAID HE CAME DOWN HERE TO GET A LITTLE WORK DONE HERE BEFORE CHRISTMAS···FOUND HIMSELF SHORT-HANDED AND HIRED ME TO HELP PULL THE SLEIGH···HIGH OVER ROOF TOP AND STEEPLE·· WE LEAVE TONIGHT FOR THE STATES.

HOW CAN YOU, A MOOSE, DO *THAT*?

WELL····I SUPPOSE IT IS A LITTLE DISHONEST··· I TOLD HIM I WAS A REINDEER.

WELL, ANYWAY···· LET'S GET GOIN'·· I'VE GOT TO BE BACK IN TIME FOR THE CHRISTMAS PAGEANT.

SURE, LET'S GO OVER TO THE SLEIGH.

THIS PART I GOT IN THE PAGEANT IS A *BIG IMPORTANT ROLE* --THE STORY IS CALLED "THE NIGHT BEFORE CHRISTMAS."

I PLAY THE PART OF "NOT-EVEN."

"*NOT EVEN?*"

SURE, YOU KNOW WHERE IT SAYS "NOT A CREATURE WAS STIRRIN', *NOT-EVEN*: A MOUSE." WELL, I'M THE "NOT-A-CREATURE" WHO IS STIRRIN'····"NOT-EVEN," THE MOUSE.

Pitifully, Wittifully,

187

OOPS! GRUNDOON IS CLAMPED HIS JAW BONES ONTO PAGE 22 AN' I CAN'T TURN TO SEE WHAT'S THE REST OF THE CAROL.

WHAT A PITIES! --QUICK! OTHERELSE YOU MUST SING WITH ONLY HALF THESE CAROL.

NO DANGER OF THAT! GRUNDOON IS ET THE ENTIRE BOOK!---TOO BAD! WE'LL JES' HAFTA DO IT THE OLD WAY.

WELL, WELL! EVERYBODY READY WITH THE NEW CAROL?

ALBERT SAY IT DON'T MAKE SENSE.

SO WE GONNA SING LAS' YEAR'S ALL OVER AGAIN.

READY!

DECK US ALL WITH BOSTON CHARLIE WALLA WALLA WASH AN' KALAMAZOO! NORA'S FREEZIN' ON THE TROLLEY SWALLER DOLLAR CAULIFLOWER, ALLEY-GA-ROO!

DON'T WE KNOW ARCHAIC BARREL? LULLABY LILLA BOY, LOUISVILLE LOU! TROLLEY MOLLY DON'T LOVE HAROLD BOOLA BOOLA PENSACOOLA HULLA-BALLOO!

NOW HOW 'BOUT "GOOD KING SAUERKRAUT, LOOK OUT! ON YO' FEETS UNEVEN WHILE THE SNOO LAY 'ROUND ABOUT..". UH-WHAT'S SNOO?

NOT MUCH, AS YOU KIN SEE.

THESE MAKES MORE SENSE?

CHAPTER

32

Plea.